I'm going to be just like Daddy!

At milking time I take care of the calves

just like Daddy does.

After that I sit with the sheep
and keep them calm
just like Daddy does.

Then I check that the horses have enough straw
just like Daddy does.

Then I bark at the top of my voice
just like Daddy does.

And when my work is done
I go to sleep under a tree